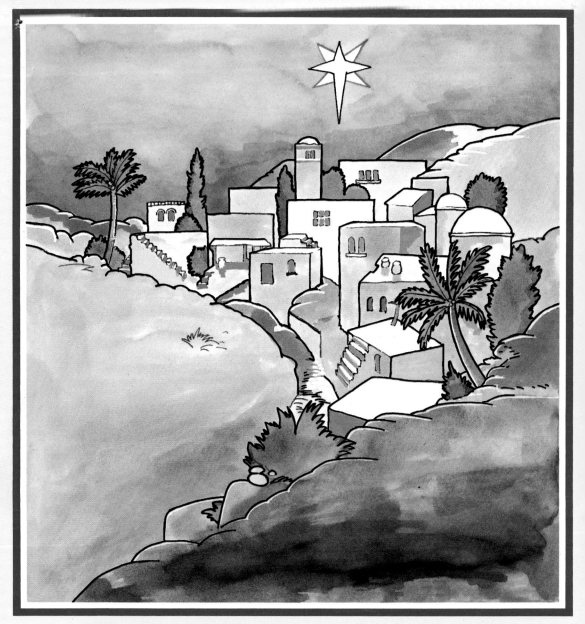

Bethlehem was full of visitors when they arrived.

Mary and Joseph lived in
the busy town of Nazareth.

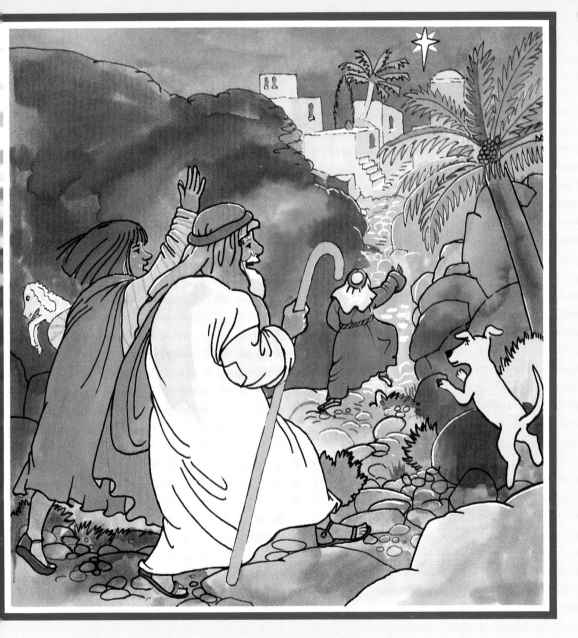

So the shepherds
hurried to Bethlehem.

There they found the
baby, lying in a
manger.

'Glory to God', the angels sang. 'Peace on earth.'

'Good news,' the angel said. 'A new-born king is born today.'

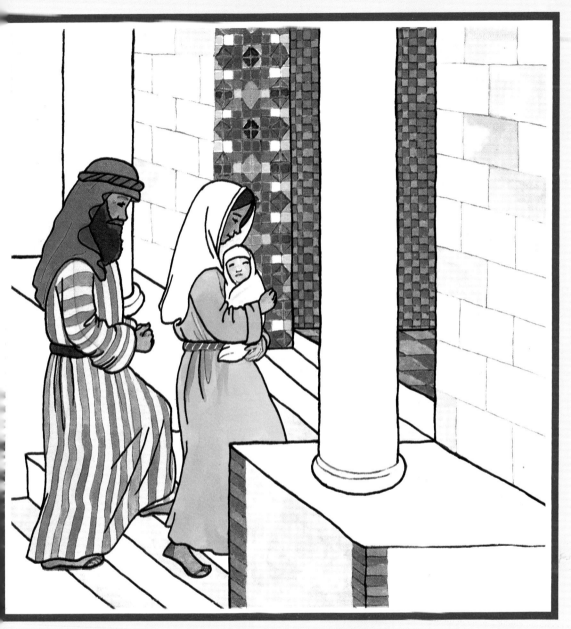

Mary and Joseph went to
the temple to thank God
for their special baby.

In the East wise men saw a special star.

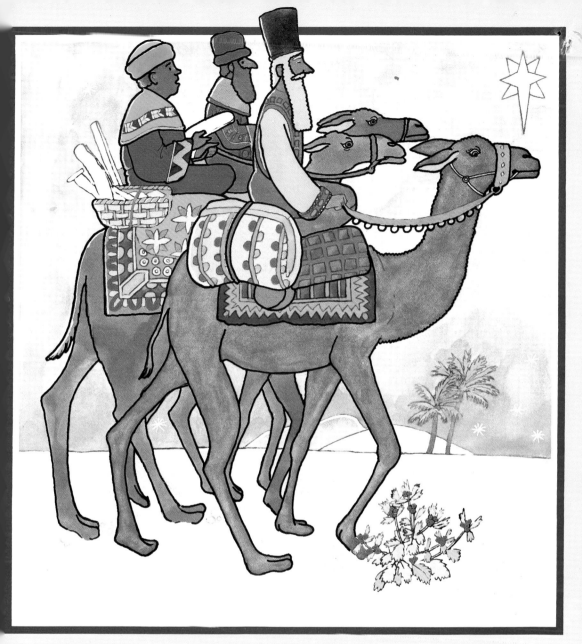

It would lead them to a
new-born king.

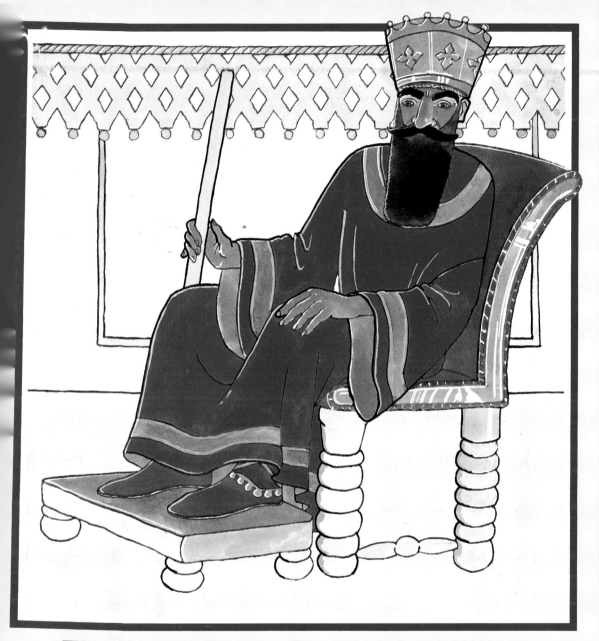

They came to Jerusalem and asked to see King Herod.

'Where is the bab
But King Herod di
worried by this ta

king?' they asked.

not know. He was

of a new king.

The wise men followed
the star to Bethlehem.

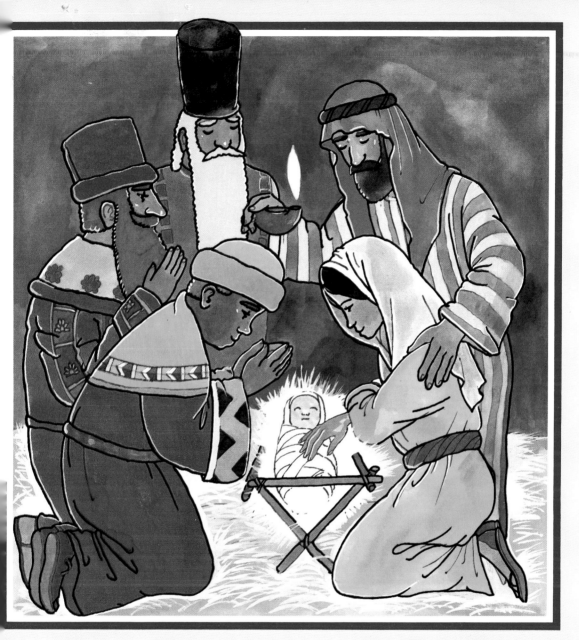

They knelt before God's
baby king, and
worshipped him.

They gave presents:
gold, frankincense and
myrrh.

Now everyone can celebrate
the birth of baby Jesus
at Christmas time each year.

FACE TO FACE WITH

LEOPARDS

by Beverly and Dereck Joubert

NATIONAL
GEOGRAPHIC

WASHINGTON, D.C.

CONTENTS

We've known this leopard, whom we call Legadema, since she was a cub. When she saw her own reflection in my lens, she wanted to play.

FACE TO FACE: INTRODUCTION

Leopards have eyes like honey and teeth like needles. Their whiskers are very sensitive.

It's not easy to come face to face with a leopard. They are usually shy and secretive. But this one was only eight days old when we spotted her. She seemed curious and bold. And back then, she didn't look fierce at all – more like a fat house cat.

My wife, Beverly, and I have been filming and photographing African wildlife for many years. We were in the Okavango Delta, in Botswana, when we first saw this leopard baby.

Legadema peers up at us as we sit in our jeep. She felt comfortable around the vehicle, and often went under it to rest in its shade.

As we admired the cub, her mother looked up and bared her teeth at us. She arched her back and came toward us. We were sitting in our jeep, which doesn't have any doors. They get in the way when we're filming. Now I wondered if that was such a good idea!

Growling, the mother leopard smelled the front of the vehicle. When she came around to my side, our eyes met. Her mouth was full of foamy spit and needle-sharp teeth. I froze. She hissed. Then she turned and went back to her cub. For the next four years, Beverly and I followed that cub as she grew up. The mother leopard never hissed at us again.

About three months later, a thunderstorm broke while the cub's mother was out hunting. Alone, the cub shivered with fear. It was her first storm. Suddenly, lightning struck the tree next to us.

I thought the cub would run away. But instead, she ran straight towards us and crouched by my feet! After that, people started calling her Legadema (pronounced lach-ah-dee-ma). In the local language of Botswana, that means "light from above", or lightning.

Legadema became a kind of friend to us. But we kept our distance. It can be dangerous for leopards and humans to get too close.

7

MEET

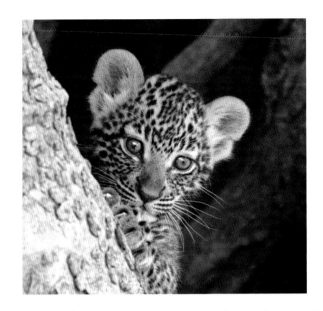

Just a few days old, Legadema peeks out on the world through steel grey eyes. As cubs grow older, their eye colour changes to amber.

THE LEOPARD

A leopard's spots and colour give it the perfect camouflage.

One day Legadema was in a curious mood. She had been watching us as we worked in the jeep. When Beverly moved to the back of the car, Legadema came up to the vehicle. Then she climbed into Beverly's seat and looked me right in the face!

We were amazed, but we knew we had to discourage this behaviour. It could be a disaster if Legadema tried it with tourists visiting the game reserve. I decided to teach her some manners the same way her mother would. I hissed at her.

9

She ignored me. Then I turned on the car heater, which made a more impressive noise. That made her leave.

Legadema is unusual. Most leopards avoid humans, although some have been known to attack and kill people. But usually these big cats prefer other **prey**, such as antelope and deer.

As the mother leopard licks her cub, she protects the cub from infection. The mum's spit, or saliva, is like an antiseptic.

Leopards are solitary animals. This means they spend most of their lives alone. Except for mating, they avoid other leopards. It's rare to see more than one leopard at a time unless it is a mother and cubs.

Leopard cubs stay with their mothers for about two years. They have a lot to learn in that time. They watch their mothers hunt. They learn which trees are best to hide in and which trunks are easy to climb.

One day, Legadema's mum brought her a present. It was an impala, a type of antelope. Legadema played with it by chasing it and pouncing on it. This game helped her practise the hunting skills she would need to survive on her own one day.

When Legadema was about 13 months old, her mother chased her away. The young leopard had been killing her own food for a while, so her mum must have known she was ready. Legadema wandered around by herself, touching and sniffing each of her mother's favourite trees. She hunted small animals. Her mother seemed to give her some space in their **territory**. We think she may even have been watching over Legadema and keeping in touch by scent and markings rather than by actually meeting.

When cats lift their young, the cubs freeze. You probably shouldn't wriggle too much when mum's sharp teeth are around your neck!

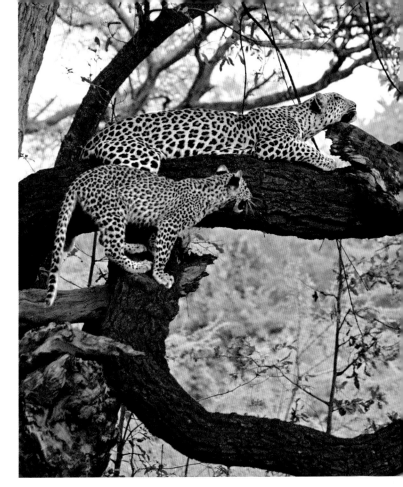

A sausage tree provides the perfect fortress for Legadema and her mom. It has lots of deep holes to hide in, and the cub can dig her claws in its soft bark and climb.

After a hard night of hunting, mum just wants to rest, but Legadema has other ideas.

Over time, Legadema found her place in the leopard world as an adult. Now she, too, is a mother.

But she hasn't forgotten us. We had been away for a while and then went back for a visit. As soon as Legadema spotted us, she came over to the car. She looked up into Beverly's eyes. Then she circled over to me and sniffed my shoe. Soon she was lying in the shade under our jeep, just like she used to.

13

Leopards catch their prey off guard by leaping to the ground from high up in the trees.

FOREST GHOSTS

This vervet monkey was just a little too slow and couldn't escape a sly leopard.

Leopards prowl the forest like ghosts. They slip through the shadows. They slink through tall grass. Even in bright sunlight, it's hard to see them. Their yellowish fur with dark spots blends into the background. This helps them hide from their prey until they are ready to pounce.

Like all big cats, leopards are **predators**. This means they hunt, kill and eat other animals to survive. Leopards eat almost anything they can catch, from birds to monkeys to Cape buffalo. Almost nothing is safe!

A leopard's powerful jaw muscles and sharp claws help it drag an impala up a tree, away from other predators that might steal it.

The leopard hunts alone. It creeps up on its prey secretly and silently. This is called **stalking**. We have watched a leopard lie in wait for hours, watching an antelope nibble grass. Slowly, the powerful cat inches closer and closer, until – wham! It springs at its prey, pins the animal down and kills it, usually with one fierce bite.

Instead of eating their catch on the spot, leopards often drag it away. They do this to get away from the lions and hyenas that might steal their meal. They stash it under a bush or haul it up into the treetops. A leopard is so strong that it can drag an animal twice its weight up a tree. It does this with the help of its powerful neck, shoulder and jaw muscles and its strong legs.

Besides being good climbers, leopards are also strong swimmers. They will catch and eat fish, crabs and other water animals – even small hippos!

Leopards have sharp eyesight and keen hearing, which help them detect prey. They usually hunt at night. But at Mombo, the region in the Okavango Delta where Legadema lives, we saw her hunt during the day and night.

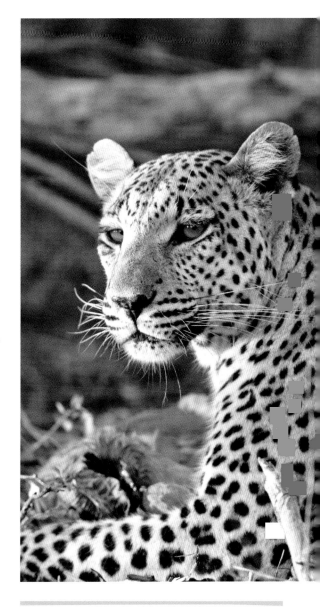

Predators eat meat, and they have to kill in order to survive. Predators and prey are a natural part of life in the wild.

Telling one leopard from another seems hard. Here are some ways researchers "spot" the difference!

- On the fat upper lip on either side of a leopard's nose are rows of dark black spots with a whisker coming out of each. The pattern of these whisker spots is different for each cat.

- Every leopard also has a unique pattern of dark spots around its neck. This band of black spots is called a necklace. In addition, researchers often use the spots on the sides of leopards' bodies to identify them.

- As a cub, Legadema had a unique spot on her upper lip that was a perfect way to identify her. She still has it today, which shows that a leopard really does not change its spots!

To us, it looks as though leopards sometimes really have fun. An adult leopard might spot a squirrel and spend an hour chasing it up and down trees, over logs, and in and out of holes. I think the big cat must enjoy the chase, since the small mouthful of fur doesn't seem like much of a reward for all that effort.

Sometimes leopards stalk and prey on baboons. But sometimes the baboons are the predators. When Legadema was a cub, we saw a troop of baboons try to drag her and her mother out of their den. A mob of baboons can rip a leopard to shreds. Legadema learned to hide or run away when she met a group of them. Lions also pose a danger to leopards. We have seen lions chase a leopard up into a tree and then try to pull it down and kill it.

Smell is important to leopards. They claw tree trunks and spray their urine on trees to leave their scent behind. This tells other leopards that the territory is theirs. This way, they can avoid others. If one leopard does see another, it will usually turn away. Leopards also roar to let other leopards know where they are. A leopard's roar sounds rather like a deep, raspy cough.

Legadema makes a quick exit when she spots these elephants looming over her.

Leopards live in many parts of Africa and Asia. A few leopards appear to be solid black. I once saw one for an instant. Within the black coat there were even darker spots, like a normal leopard has. This is different from what is commonly known as a black panther, which is often a black jaguar or even a dark mountain lion. No matter what their overall colour is, leopards are expert at disappearing. It's almost as if they have Harry Potter's invisibility cloak!

Legadema scans the treetops for squirrels. Hunting them became an obsession for her.

LEOPARD LEGACY

As a cub, Legadema loved to play. She just had to watch out for her mum's sharp teeth and claws – and that stinky cat breath!

Leopards live in more climates and **habitats** than any other big cat. They live in Africa, Central Asia, India, Russia and China. They live in forests, grasslands, deserts and mountains. They survive in warm climates and in cold. In fact, leopards can **adapt** to nearly any habitat. In some parts of the world, they even live in suburban areas. They just need a place to hide in and hunt.

But even though they are very adaptable, they still face many problems. One of the biggest is habitat loss. As human populations grow, we take over land that was once wild, and the animals lose their habitat.

When there are baboons in the area, Legadema returns to a safe place.

Leopards aren't the only big cats with spots. Jaguars and cheetahs have them, too. Here's how to spot the difference.

 A leopard's spots group together to form clusters. These are called rosettes, because they look a bit like a rose. The rosettes do not have a dot in the center.

 The jaguar's coat is patterned with rings of small black spots. The rings are also called rosettes. They often have a black dot in the center.

 The spots on a cheetah's coat are solid. They are evenly spaced and do not form rosettes.

When leopards live near human settlements, they may prey on dogs and on **livestock** such as cattle. To protect their animals, farmers shoot, trap or poison the big cats. In some places, wildlife conservation groups pay cattle owners for livestock that leopards kill, as long as the owners don't kill the cats.

Leopards face another challenge. Some African countries still allow leopard hunting. Leopards are hunted for their valuable fur coats. They are also killed for their tails, claws and whiskers, which are used in some traditional medicines.

She's fully grown now, but we can usually still find Legadema in the same trees she liked to climb as a cub.

Permits are issued, allowing only a certain number of leopards to be hunted worldwide. But we think it's still too many, because no one knows how many are killed by **poachers**, who hunt illegally, without permits.

Leopards are very difficult to see, let alone count, but we know their numbers are declining. Today, some conservationists think there may be as few as 50,000 mature leopards, but we need more information. In some parts of the world, especially Asia, the leopard is already on the verge of extinction.

◄ *Legadema perches
confidently on a branch,
queen of all she surveys.*

Leopards play an important role in the wild. Without the top predators, the number of prey **species** would go out of balance. There would be so many prey animals that soon they would have trouble finding food. They would damage the environment by eating too much plant life. So predators are important to the balance of nature. They prey on the weaker members of a herd, making the herd stronger. They keep them on the move, fit and alert, always ready to flee from those spots in the grass that just might be a leopard in disguise.

Today, many people are turning against hunting, and many national parks protect the big cats. Tourism also helps by raising money for conservation and helping people appreciate wildlife. We are very hopeful that in time more people will learn to value these precious animals and that their populations will start to recover.

Helping leopards starts with understanding them. Learn all you can about these big cats. You are already off to a good start! Read about leopards in books and magazines and on the internet. Watch documentary films and TV programmes about them. Visit leopards in zoos. The more you learn about leopards, the more you will appreciate them. You might even come to love them as deeply as we do.

Talk to everyone you can about leopards and share what you've learned. Someone who is passionate about something and who knows a lot about the subject can have a lot of influence.

Leopards have keen eyesight.

Support conservation groups that protect big cats. For example, the World Wildlife Fund (WWF) and the African Wildlife Foundation have up-to-date information on leopard conservation on their websites. So does the National Geographic Big Cat Initiative, which we founded. It raises funds for emergency help for lions, leopards, cheetahs and tigers. And it is working. A few years ago, when we started the programme, one area in Kenya was losing 40 lions a year and countless leopards. A year later, the programme had helped limit the losses to just one lion and no leopards at all.

Think about how to raise money to help conservation organisations keep big cats safe. Rally your classmates, teachers, friends and families. Encourage them to go on the website of one of these groups and donate whatever they can afford. Every little bit helps to keep these cats from dying out.

You can help preserve the world's wild places for leopards and other wildlife by doing what you can to reduce the impact you have on the natural world each day. Don't waste water. Recycle whatever you can. The fewer forests that are chopped down to make paper products, for example, the more space there will be for all wildlife to survive.

Not everyone gets the chance to see leopards face to face in the wild. Fortunately, several zoos have leopard exhibits where you can watch the great cats firsthand. But to get a sense of what it's like to track leopards in the wild, you don't have to go any further than a local park or your own garden. Like the forests of Africa, these places are telling a wonderful tale. You just need to pay attention.

1 Listen. We find many leopards just by listening to the other animals. Calling birds, screeching squirrels and screaming monkeys all sound the alarm when a leopard is nearby. The next time you're outside, listen to what's going on. If the birds suddenly start squawking, there could be a cat slinking along nearby.

2 Watch closely. All cats like to hide, whether they're hundred-pound leopards or eight-pound house cats. It's the way they stalk and hunt. Sometimes, if we keep looking at the spot the birds are showing us, we suddenly see a beautiful pair of amber eyes looking back. In the park or garden, you might spot a pair of cat eyes peering out from the bushes.

3 Move slowly. Never move directly towards the cat. To cats, fast approaches are rude. And if you don't know the cat, do not get too close! Leave the way you came, slowly and quietly.

Happy tracking!

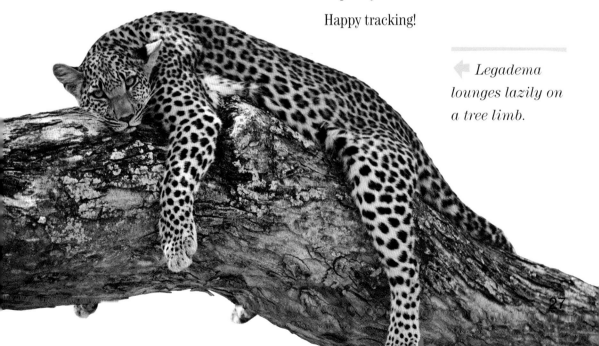

← *Legadema lounges lazily on a tree limb.*

27

Scientific Name

Leopards belong to the cat family, called *Felidae*. The species name is *Panthera pardus*.

Common Name

There are several different varieties, or subspecies, of leopards. Some are named after the place they come from, such as the Chinese leopard, which lives in northern China. Despite their names, the snow leopard (*Panthera uncia*) and the clouded leopard (*Neofelis nebulosa*) are not true leopards.

Life Span

In the wild, leopards live 12 to 17 years. In captivity they have been known to live 23 years.

⬇ *Legadema and her mom patrolling their territory.*

Size

Leopards weigh 30 to 80 kilograms. Males are heavier than females. Leopards vary in length from 91 to 191 centimetres; tails are about 58 to 110 centimetres long.

Diet

Leopards are meat eaters, or carnivores. They eat a wide variety of animals, including antelope, deer, squirrels and other rodents, birds, monkeys, baboons, fish, reptiles and porcupines. We have seen them kill 33 species of wildlife in the area of Africa that we study. Leopards will also eat meat killed by other animals. I've even seen a leopard eating an elephant! One day some lions were eating an old elephant when a male leopard snuck in quietly and joined the feast.

Reproduction

Females are pregnant for about three and a half months before they give birth. They usually have litters of two to three cubs. Life as a baby leopard can be tough. Legadema's mother lost five previous cubs to hyenas, baboons, and other predators before Legadema was born.

Habitat and Range

These adaptable cats live in a wide variety of habitats – rainforests, open woodlands, dry grasslands, plains, deserts and mountains. They can survive in cold and warm climates.

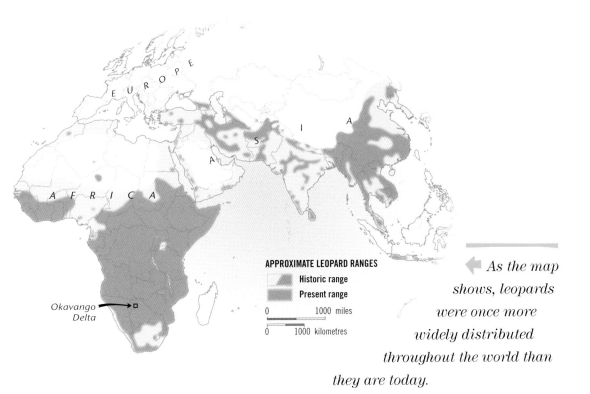

APPROXIMATE LEOPARD RANGES

Historic range

Present range

0   1000 miles

0   1000 kilometres

Okavango Delta

As the map shows, leopards were once more widely distributed throughout the world than they are today.

They live in sub-Saharan Africa, northeast Africa, the Arabian Peninsula, the Middle East, Central Asia, India and China.

Biggest Threats

Loss of habitat is one of the biggest threats to leopards' survival. Their habitats are being destroyed for logging and farming and to make way for roads and houses. Leopards are also being shot, trapped, or poisoned by farmers who believe the big cats are killing their livestock. Hunters and poachers kill the big cats for sport or for their fur and other body parts.

Status in the Wild

The number of leopards living in the wild has declined greatly in the last hundred years, and it continues to decrease. Today, some conservationists estimate that about 50 000 mature leopards exist in the wild. While they are still fairly numerous in some places, such as parts of southern Africa, in other places leopards are **endangered**.

The rarest leopard of all is probably the Amur leopard. It was once found throughout the Korea Peninsula, northeastern China and southeastern Russia. Now it is extinct in South Korea. Only a handful of Amur leopards are left in the mountainous regions of China and Russia. Researchers estimate that there are fewer than 50 of them living in the wild today.

Adapt: To become suited to one's surroundings. Animals can adapt to changes in the environment over many generations.

Endangered: A species with very few individuals remaining. If the number of individuals rises, the classification may change to "threatened" or "recovered". If the number falls, the species may become "extinct," meaning no individuals are left.

Habitat: The local environment in which an animal lives.

Livestock: Animals such as cattle or sheep that are kept and raised by humans.

Poacher: A person who takes or kills an animal illegally.

Predator: An animal that hunts, kills and then feeds on other animals.

Prey: An animal that is hunted for food.

Range: The area in which an animal lives.

Species: A group of animals or plants that look similar, can breed with one another, and have offspring who can also breed successfully.

Stalk: To hunt or track secretly and quietly.

Territory: An area that an animal, or a group of animals, lives in and defends from other animals of the same species.

Researching and working in one of the world's most beautiful places is like a dream come true. And for us, a day spent tracking a tiny leopard cub is a perfect day. Each day we find ourselves snapping awake in the dark, usually around 4 o'clock in the morning, eager to get out and find her. We tumble out of bed, pull on clothes already laid out the night before, shake out shoes in case any scorpions have crawled in, and shove all our stuff into steel trunks so the mice don't get in. Then we zip the tent closed behind us, to stop baboons or monkeys from sneaking in and stealing our things. Nowadays, we have to double lock the zippers because they have become so clever!

Then we head out in our jeep. Beverly stands up through a roof hatch, searching, listening to the forest, while I scan the track ahead for the slightest shape of footprints or a movement in the brush.

Legadema has favourite trees to lie in, so we check those. Once we find her, that's it for us for the day. What she does, we do.

Our vehicle is our office, so we keep a lot of cameras spread around, ready for action. We have a section for food, books, journals, hot water for tea, and cold water for the midday heat – which can reach 130 degrees. There is a mosquito net that we couldn't live without. Hats, sunscreen, sunglasses, night glasses for driving when the bugs are out, a sound recorder, and microphones that can pick up a leopard panting at 50 yards. We also have sleeping bags – sometimes in winter it can go below freezing at night.

Our vehicle is our best friend, just as a horse is a cowboy's best friend. Sadly, I don't treat it very well. I drive it in places where no vehicle is meant to go – into valleys of mud that people can't walk through, over rocks to the tops of hills, and across rivers so deep the water comes up over my belt as I sit driving.

This kind of life is not for everyone. But for people who want adventure, it's the best life there is.

– DJ & BJ

Published by Collins
An imprint of HarperCollins*Publishers*
The News Building
1 London Bridge Street, London, SE1 9GF

HarperCollins *Publishers*
1st Floor, Watermarque Building, Ringsend Road,
Doublin 4, Ireland

Browse the complete Collins catalogue at
www.collins.co.uk

In association with National Geographic Partners, LLC

NATIONAL GEOGRAPHIC and the Yellow Border Design
are trademarks of the National Geographic Society, used
under license.

British English edition 2019
First published 2009

ISBN 978-0-00-835816-7

10 9 8 7 6 5 4 3

British English Edition
Commissioning editor: Sarah Thomas
Content editor: Alexandra Wells
Educational reviewer: Catherine Baker
Design and typesetting: 2Hoots Publishing Services Ltd
Proof reader: Gaynor Spry
Production controller: Rachel Weaver
Printed and bound by: Replika Press Pvt. Ltd.

To the 10,000 leopards that have given their lives to the vanity
of man since we first met Legadema, and the countless number
fallen to the poacher's guns … and to a little leopard with
mischief in her eyes. – DJ & BJ

Acknowledgments

We looked into the eyes of one little leopard one day and our
lives were changed forever. She stole our hearts in a way that
makes our hearts swell. We developed a trust with her that
very few humans even have with another human being. I have
seldom been in the company of such greatness in one character,
or such beauty and it is a leopard. The other more enduring
beauty in my life is Beverly, as rare a creature as a leopard, and
I have to thank both of these wonderous females. We mutually
thank the country and citizens of Botswana for keeping spaces
enough to house these phantoms of the forest.
– DJ & BJ

The publisher wishes to thank Dr Andrew Stein, Research
Coordinator of the Predator Conservation Trust, for his
review of the map and text For their important contributions
on leopard distribution for the map, we thank Chris and Tilde
Stuart, Rachel Ikemeh and Farid Belbachir. Arezoo Sanei
contributed information from her 2008 work, *Analysis of
leopard* (Panthera pardus) *status in Iran (No. 1)*. Tehran:
Sepeher Publication Center. Second edition. P. 71.

Additional photo credits:

P. 22 centre left: Steve Winter/National GeographicStock.com;
p. 22 bottom left: Andrew Dowsett/iStock
Photo.com.

If you would like to comment on any aspect of this book,
please contact us at the above address or online.
natgeokidsbooks.co.uk
collins.reference@harpercollins.co.uk

Since 1888, the National Geographic Society has funded more
than 12,000 research, exploration and preservation projects
around the world. The Society receives funds from National
Geographic Partners, LLC, funded in part by your purchase. A
portion of the proceeds from this book supports this vital work.
To learn more, visit natgeo.com/info.

Beverly and Dereck Joubert are National Geographic
Explorers-in-Residence, filmmakers, researchers, authors
and photographers who have worked in the field in Africa for
30 years. They are experts in big cats and have just spent five
years working with leopards in Botswana. They have earned
five Emmys and a Peabody for their film work and were
recently honoured with the World Ecology Award from the
University of Missouri. They have written and photographed six
books and many articles for *National Geographic* magazine.
The Jouberts feel that their achievements are a result of their
being able to live permanently in the bush and get close to
wildlife, face to face.